Guest Spot

GERSHWIN
Playalong *for* Flute

Wise Publications
part of The Music Sales Group
London/New York/Paris/Sydney/Copenhagen/Berlin/Madrid/Tokyo

Published by
Wise Publications
14-15 Berners Street, London W1T 3LJ, UK.

Exclusive Distributors:
Music Sales Limited
Distribution Centre, Newmarket Road, Bury St Edmunds,
Suffolk IP33 3YB, UK.
Music Sales Pty Limited
20 Resolution Drive,
Caringbah, NSW 2229, Australia.

Order No. AM995192
ISBN 13: 978-1-84772-700-8
This book © Copyright 2008 Wise Publications,
a division of Music Sales Limited.

Not for sale in France or Spain.

Arranging and engraving supplied by Camden Music.
Edited by Sam Harrop.
Compiled by Nick Crispin.

Printed in the EU.

CD recorded, mixed and mastered by Jonas Persson.
Flute played by John Whelan.

Your Guarantee of Quality:
As publishers, we strive to produce every book to
the highest commercial standards.
The music has been freshly engraved and the book has been
carefully designed to minimise awkward page turns and
to make playing from it a real pleasure.
Particular care has been given to specifying acid-free, neutral-sized
paper made from pulps which have not been elemental chlorine bleached.
This pulp is from farmed sustainable forests and was
produced with special regard for the environment.
Throughout, the printing and binding have been planned to
ensure a sturdy, attractive publication which should give years of enjoyment.
If your copy fails to meet our high standards,
please inform us and we will gladly replace it.

www.musicsales.com

Flute Fingering Chart

But Not For Me (from *Girl Crazy*)

Music by George Gershwin

I Got Rhythm (from *Girl Crazy*)

Music by George Gershwin

I'll Build A Stairway To Paradise

(from *George White's Scandals Of 1922*)

Music by George Gershwin

Love Walked In (from *The Goldwyn Follies*)

Music by George Gershwin

The Man I Love (from *Lady, Be Good*)

Music by George Gershwin

Tenderly, straight quavers ♩ = 63

Oh, Lady Be Good! (from *Lady, Be Good*)

Music by George Gershwin

Suddenly faster, with a bounce ♩ = 98

19

Someone To Watch Over Me (from *Oh, Kay!*)

Music by George Gershwin

Summertime (from *Porgy And Bess*)

Music by George Gershwin

They Can't Take That Away From Me

(from *Shall We Dance?*)

Music by George Gershwin

With a lazy swing ♩ = 116

Nice Work If You Can Get It

(from *A Damsel In Distress*)

Music by George Gershwin

Più mosso

♩ = 160

(drum solo)

123456789